It's for You, Snoopy

Charles M. Schulz

Selected cartoons from
Sunday's Fun Day, Charlie Brown, Vol. 1

Adam Moore

A FAWCETT CREST BOOK

Fawcett Publications, Inc., Greenwich, Conn.

Only 50¢ Each—Wherever Paperbacks Are Sold

If your bookdealer is sold out, send cover price plus 15¢ each for postage
and handling to Mail Order Department, Fawcett Publications, Inc.,
Greenwich, Connecticut 06803. Please order by number and title. No
Canadian orders. Catalog available on request.

IT'S FOR YOU, SNOOPY

This book, prepared especially for Fawcett Publications, Inc.,
comprises the first half of *SUNDAY'S FUN DAY, CHARLIE
BROWN,* and is reprinted by arrangement with Holt, Rinehart &
Winston, Inc.

Published by Fawcett World Library
67 West 44th Street, New York, N.Y. 10036
Printed in the United States of America
May 1971

I'M GOING IN FOR LUNCH, SNOOPY... HOLD THIS FOR ME...

WHATEVER YOU DO, DON'T LET GO OF IT!

DIDN'T SEE ANY, HUH? NEITHER DID I...

SNOOPY AND I HAVE BEEN OUT HUNTING RABBITS, BUT WE DIDN'T SEE ANY

NOW WHAT WAS THAT ALL ABOUT?

ORDINARILY, I FROWN ON CARD PLAYING, BUT BRIDGE IS A PRETTY GOOD GAME, AND, AFTER ALL, THEY DO NEED A PLACE TO PLAY...

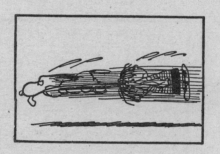

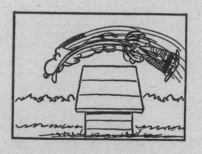

I WONDER IF MY BIRD TENANTS HAVE LEARNED HOW TO FLY YET...

PLUNK!

SIT UP, SNOOPY, AND I'LL GIVE YOU A NICE PIECE OF CANDY...

HUMPF!

"SIT UP, SNOOPY, AND I'LL GIVE YOU A NICE PIECE OF CANDY."....PHOOEY! WHO NEEDS IT?!

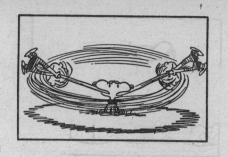

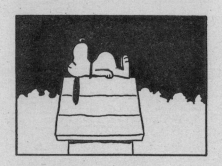

IT'S A LIVING!

THIS IS GOING TO BE ONE OF THOSE DAYS WHEN WE GET NOTHING BUT SINGLES

PTUI!

UNTIL IT IS DEMONSTRATED, ONE FORGETS THE REALLY GREAT DIFFERENCE THAT EXISTS BETWEEN THE MERELY COMPETENT AMATEUR AND THE VERY EXPERT PROFESSIONAL

I WISH SHE'D INVITE ME OVER TO HER HOUSE SOME TIME. I WISH SHE'D COME UP TO ME, AND SAY, "WHY DON'T YOU COME OVER TO MY HOUSE AFTER SCHOOL, CHARLIE BROWN?"

THERE SHE IS AGAIN..SHE WENT INTO THE BACK YARD, AND SHE'S SWINGING ON HER SWING-SET...

WE COULD WALK HOME FROM SCHOOL TOGETHER, AND THEN WE COULD SWING ON HER SWING-SET...

BOY, WHAT A BLOCKHEAD I AM! I'LL NEVER GET TO SWING WITH HER! I'LL NEVER GET TO WALK WITH HER! I'LL NEVER EVEN GET TO SAY ONE WORD TO HER!

ALL I GET TO DO IS WALK HOME FROM SCHOOL BY MYSELF, AND...

OH, HI, SNOOPY

YOU'RE NOT MUCH OF A SUBSTITUTE FOR A LITTLE RED-HAIRED GIRL

QUITE OFTEN LATELY I HAVE THE FEELING I DON'T KNOW WHAT'S GOING ON...

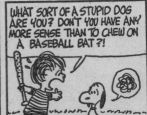

HERE'S THE FIERCE MOUNTAIN LION WAITING FOR HIS VICTIM...

WELL, ARE YOU GOING TO START SOMETHING, OR AREN'T YOU?

YOU THINK I'M AFRAID, DON'T YOU?

WELL, I'M NOT! WHEN IT COMES TO SNOWBALL WARS, I'M AN EXPERT!

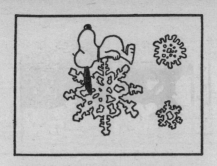

Happiness is catching snowflakes on your tongue.